Enid Blyton's

WOODLAND TALES

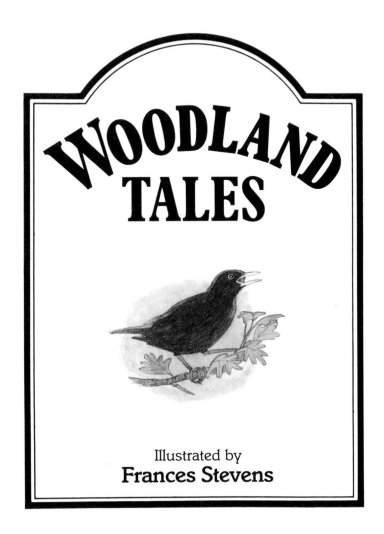

Illustrated by
Frances Stevens

AWARD PUBLICATIONS LIMITED
LONDON

ISBN 0-86163-694-5

Text copyright © 1935 Darrell Waters Limited
Illustrations copyright © 1994 by Award Publications Limited

Enid Blyton's signature is a trademark of Darrell Waters Limited

First published 1994
Published by Award Publications Limited,
Goodyear House, 52-56 Osnaburgh Street,
London NW1 3NS

Printed in Singapore

CONTENTS

ONE DARK NIGHT

SPRING was coming in and the woodland was beginning to show bunches of green leaves here and there. The starry stitchworts were out and in the damp ditch below the stinging-nettles threw up fresh green shoots. All the sleepers were awake now and enjoying the warm sunshine, the soft spring showers and the feathery breezes. The snails crept out of their hiding-places, first melting the hard plate they had grown as a winter door over the opening to their shells. The rain washed them clean and their shells shone like new. Everywhere there was beauty and freshness. The birds sang madly and all day long there was a hunting in the hedges and bushes for good nesting-places. The oak-tree was happy because a thrush, a chaffinch and a blackbird had all chosen to build their nests in its branches, although as yet there were no leaves showing from the clusters of big and little buds.

The woodland folk were often puzzled by a loud shouting and barking, by the galloping of hooves and the appearance over the

hill beyond of a crowd of excited human creatures. At the first sounds the rabbits fled to their burrows, the toad hopped under his stone and the hedgehog rolled himself up tightly. None of them knew that a fox was being hunted; they simply feared the strange cries and unexpected noise.

A few days back a curious thing had happened. The noise had come suddenly nearer, and across the field streamed a line of horses, following a great crowd of baying hounds. They were chasing the red fox that lived in the woods. He tore up to a hedgerow, slipped through it and out on the other side. The hounds squeezed through the hedge after him, but the horsemen had to go round to the old gate. The fox ran to the stream that bounded the farther field, jumped in it, and ran up the water for a good way. Then, having thus cleverly broken his trail for the hounds behind him, he slipped out of the water on the same side as he had jumped in, and made his way back to the hedgerow under cover of the tall weeds growing on a near-by bank. The hounds were puzzled to lose the fox's trail and began to sniff about the bank of the stream, some of them jumping in.

The fox dragged himself to the hedgerow, his breath coming in great gasps, for he had run a great many miles. He had hurt his leg on some barbed wire and it pained him.

He sat down and licked it, but the noise of the hounds frightened him again. He looked up and down the hedge-bank for a safe place and found a large hole leading to a rabbit's burrow. Limping painfully he went up to it and, knowing well that he could not run any farther, squeezed himself into the hole and made his way in as far as he could.

The rabbits were terrified. 'Fox! Fox!' went the word along the burrows. But they need not have minded, for the red fox was too tired and too weak to do anything to harm them. He listened for the hounds, but they had lost the trail and wandered off in another direction, having found the scent of another fox that had passed that way the night before. The hidden fox was safe for the moment.

He lay in hiding for a few days. His leg swelled up and he could not use it. He dragged himself out of the hole to drink water from the pond, and he snapped up a small bird that had fallen from its nest in the hedge. He was in pain and he was anxious about his mate, the vixen, who lived with him in his earth on the other side of the wood.

One dark night the fox crept out of the burrow and sniffed to windward. A strange smell came to him. He puzzled his head as to what it could be. It was not hare, nor rabbit; not stoat, nor weasel; it was . . . it was badger!

The fox gave a soft bark and the badger answered him with a grunt. They had met before, these two nightprowlers. The badger ran up to the fox and sniffed him over. The fox could barely see him, for it was very dark, but the starlight gave enough glimmer for him to spy the striped black and white face of the big badger.

'Your mate has been howling for you,' said the badger to the fox. 'Where have you been?'

'I was hunted and hurt my leg,' said the fox. 'I have been hiding in this hole. I have not seen you for a long time, badger. Where have you been?'

'I have slept most of the winter,' answered the badger, scratching at a heap of leaves, hoping to find a toad underneath, for he was hungry. 'I always sleep in the cold weather, for then it is so difficult to find food.'

'It's easy if you know where the early lambs are and where the chickens go to roost in the farmer's shed,' said the fox. 'I never sleep in the winter. Did you make yourself a hole somewhere?'

'Yes,' said the badger. 'I scraped an enormous hole in the woodland bank. My feet are very strong and my claws can cut through the roots of bushes and trees easily, if I come across them in my digging. I made a very deep hole, far beneath the surface and I dug out three or four entrances to my winter home in case I should be caught by an enemy!'

'I shouldn't like to go to sleep in a hole that had three or four passages to it!' said the fox. 'That seems stupid to me.'

'Well, I blocked up all the entrances before I went to sleep there with my family, of course.' said the badger. ' I am not so stupid as to forget to do that! We were very cosy indeed, I can tell you! Even during that very cold spell, when thick ice covered all the ponds, we were warm and comfortable. I piled great heaps of moss and leaves into my winter home and we slept softly on those. But now that we are awake again, I have been cleaning out my hole. You should see the great pile of stuff that I have dragged outside! I hate dirty bedding. I am a clean creature – not like you, fox, for you always smell unpleasant to me!'

'If you leave great piles of your winter bedding outside your hole every one will know where you live and you will be hunted, as I have been,' said the fox.

'No, the badgers are not hunted like you,' said the badger, quietly. 'We do not kill lambs and chickens as you do, fox. We dare not meddle with the human creatures and their belongings.'

'Will you tell my mate that I will return to her tomorrow night?' asked the fox. 'I must not leave this hiding-place until I can run fast again, in case I meet a dog who will chase me.'

'I will tell her if you will do something for me,' said the badger.

'Tell me where I can find a rabbit's nest. I love rooting up a nest of young rabbits. They make a fine dinner.'

12

'I think there is one under that clump of bracken yonder,' said the fox. The badger went off, licking his lips. He was a clumsy, lumbering creature, but he made no sound as he went. He smelt under the bracken and then began to dig a hole with his claws. They were so sharp and so strong that in a moment or two he had dug a deep hole – but there was no sign of a nest there, although his sharp nose could smell the scent of young rabbits.

He went back to the fox.

'There are no rabbits there,' he said.

'There were yesterday,' said the fox. 'I saw the mother go to them.'

'She has taken them away!' cried a small, sharp voice, and a little weasel looked through a hole in the hedgerow. 'She was afraid because you were here, fox, so when you slept in your hole she took each of her rabbits and hid them in the big burrow on the the other side of the hedge. I know, because I met her carrying one and I ate it.'

'Interfering little creature,' muttered the fox, angrily, as the weasel ran snickering along the other side of the hedge. There was no love lost between the two, for very often they hunted along the same ground and stole each other's prey.

'You deceived me,' said the badger to the fox. 'You must have known the rabbit had taken away her young ones. You are sly

and cunning, fox, I shall not go to tell your mate you are hiding here safely. I shall tell her that you are dead in a trap, and she must go to seek another fox to live with.'

'If you do that,' said the fox, his bright eyes glinting fiercely, 'I will find my mate to-morrow, and we shall make our nest in the upper passages of your home. You do not like our smell, and you will be forced to leave your comfortable hole and make a fresh one. Your family will not like that.'

The badger snorted angrily. It was true that he could not bear the musky smell of the fox. He was a very clean animal, and he considered the fox a dirty and unpleasant companion, no matter how beautiful his red coat was, or how magnificent his fine brush-tail! He remembered clearly that two winters ago he and his family had all had to leave their comfortable home deep in the earth because two foxes had come to live in one of the tunnels leading to his big, hidden chamber. After the badger family had gone the foxes had taken possession of the cosy hole, so well lined with moss and leaves, and had brought up a family of six little cubs there. The badger remembered this, and snapped angrily at the fox, who at once retreated into the hole behind him. He feared the badger's strong, interlocking teeth.

'I will tell your mate what you say,' growled the badger at last. 'But you must promise me not to come near my home, for we badgers are clean and cannot live with you foxes.'

'I promise,' said the fox, yawning. What did he care where he and his mate lived? There were plenty of holes to take from the rabbits! They need go to no trouble for themselves. If the rabbits objected, then they would be eaten!

The badger went lumbering off, grunting. His striped face shone strangely in the darkness. The fox lay comfortably in his hole. To-morrow his leg would be healed. He could go back to his mate. Together they would go to the farmer's fowl-run and force their way into the shed. Then they would have a wonderful feast. The fox shut his eyes and dreamed happily.

The next day he was gone and the hedgerow came alive again. Rabbits hopped about freely, rejoicing that their enemy was gone. The hare ran up once or twice. The mice chattered in squeaky voices and the birds were glad that there was now no enemy beneath the hedge, waiting to snatch up their helpless young ones when they fell. And soon every one forgot the fox and no longer feared him.

Only the badger was angry – the fox and his mate had broken their promise after all, and had made their home in one of the tunnels leading to his set. The badger could not bear their smell and soon, with angry grunts and growls, he was busy pushing his family out into the moonlight. They must find another home!

THE END

CREEPY CREATURES

ONE bright sunny morning, when the birds were busy taking food to their young ones in the woodland and the little mice were scuttling about in their secret passages under the grasses, the blackbird gave his rattling cry of alarm.

'Beware! An enemy! I see him in the ditch! Beware!'

At the first notes of the blackbird's cry all the little birds fell silent and those sitting on their nest crouched very still. The mice shot into their holes and stayed there. The big toad who was crawling along at the bottom of the ditch squatted perfectly still as if he had frozen to the ground. The hedgehog on the bank stood still and peered down into the ditch below.

'It's only a snake!' he called to the toad. 'Who's afraid of a grass-snake? I'm not!'

'Well, I'm not either,' said the toad. 'I can make myself taste horrible, so that if a snake picks me up in his mouth he has to spit me out again!'

'Ssssssssss!' came the voice of the long grass-snake in the ditch. 'Ssssssssss!'

The snake raised his head, and looked around him with his gold-gleaming eyes. He was olive-green and nearly one and a half metres in length. He had a graceful, tapering tail and from his mouth there darted out his black, forked tongue. Behind his head he had bright orange patches that looked like a collar.

A small rabbit, peeping through the hedge, saw the snake's black tongue, and shivered. 'Is that its sting?' he asked an older rabbit.

'Sting!' said the rabbit, scornfully, 'don't be so ignorant! That's only a tongue. The snake uses it to feel things. I've often seen that snake run its tongue over something. But it darts it in and out like that just to frighten us. Don't be afraid of that snake, youngster; it won't harm you. You're too big. It can only eat things by swallowing them, and it could never swallow you, you're too fat!'

'But don't snakes sting?' asked the fat young rabbit. 'I'm sure they do! I've heard the frogs say so.'

'Don't listen to those stupid creatures,' said the old rabbit.
'There's a snake that bites most poisonously, but that's not the
grass-snake yonder. He has no poison in his fangs. He's quite
harmless to us. It's the adder that bites, but he's quite different
from the grass-snake.'

'Where does the adder . . .' began the little fat rabbit, but he
didn't finish what he was saying, for the old rabbit suddenly gave
a thump with his hind feet, shot round and dived for his burrow.
The little rabbit saw his white bobtail jerking up and down, a
signal for him to run too. He rushed to his hole and then, turning
round, looked out to see what all the excitement was.
He saw another snake gliding over the grass towards them, and
at the same moment the blackbird gave another loud cry.

'An adder! An adder! Beware !'

The grass-snake heard the blackbird's cry and looked towards
the adder. 'Good-day,' he said, surprised. 'Why have you left the
warm common and come to this damp ditch?'

' I have a fancy for a frog-meal,' said the adder, his short black
tongue flickering in and out. 'I have fed on lizards for the past
week and I need a change.'

'I am not so sure I like your company,' said the grass-snake.

'Why is that?' asked the adder, his coppery eyes gleaming
angrily. 'I will not harm you.'

'I know that,' said the grass-snake. 'But I am so often mistaken
for you that I am quite afraid of knowing you. You are poisonous
and the two-legged folk kill you. I am not poisonous. I am quite
harmless, a gentle and friendly creature and I dislike being
mistaken for a fierce creature like you.'

'There is no reason why any one should mistake you for me!'
said the adder.'Look at us! We are quite different! I am much less
than a metre long and you are much longer. I am thick and
stocky and you are graceful and tapering. And look at the large
scales on your head! Mine are very small and I never wear your
orange or white collar.'

18

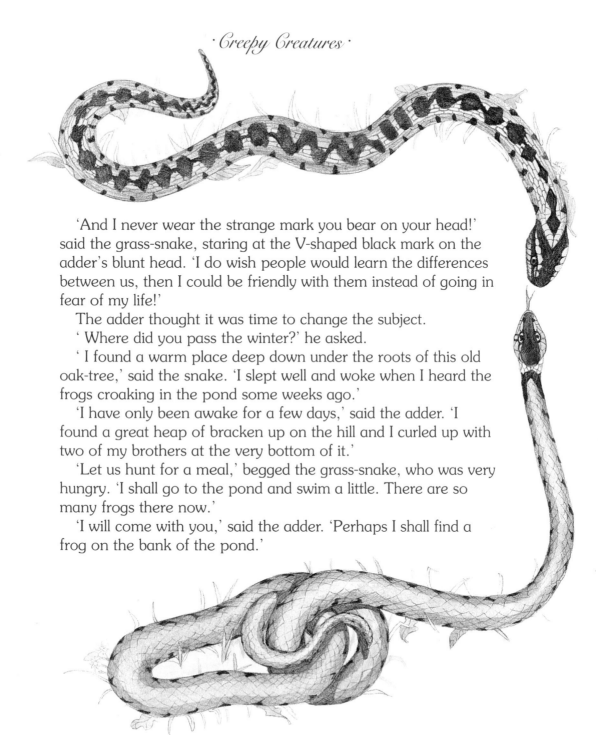

'And I never wear the strange mark you bear on your head!' said the grass-snake, staring at the V-shaped black mark on the adder's blunt head. 'I do wish people would learn the differences between us, then I could be friendly with them instead of going in fear of my life!'

The adder thought it was time to change the subject.

' Where did you pass the winter?' he asked.

' I found a warm place deep down under the roots of this old oak-tree,' said the snake. 'I slept well and woke when I heard the frogs croaking in the pond some weeks ago.'

'I have only been awake for a few days,' said the adder. 'I found a great heap of bracken up on the hill and I curled up with two of my brothers at the very bottom of it.'

'Let us hunt for a meal,' begged the grass-snake, who was very hungry. 'I shall go to the pond and swim a little. There are so many frogs there now.'

'I will come with you,' said the adder. 'Perhaps I shall find a frog on the bank of the pond.'

The two snakes glided off together and the hedgehog lifted up his voice and called rudely after them. The snakes stopped in anger. They hissed and their tongues flickered in and out. The hedgehog showed himself and began to amble towards them. He was not at all afraid.

'I like a snake for a meal! I like a snake for a meal!' he called. The snakes looked at him for a moment and then glided quickly towards the pond.

The grass-snake slipped into the water and swam swiftly here and there, darting at the unwary frogs. He caught one and came to the bank with it in his mouth. He lay down in the sun and began to swallow it. It could not get away because the hooked, backward-pointing teeth inside the snake's mouth held it too tightly.

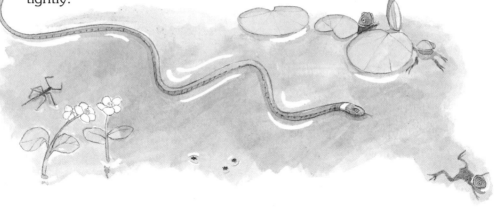

Meantime the adder had spied a fat newt. He darted his head forward like lightning and caught the newt in his jaws. The grass-snake saw his fangs stand erect as he struck and knew that poison had been pressed into the newt's body. It was killed by the poison and the hungry adder swallowed the lifeless creature eagerly.

Both snakes lay in the hot sun, digesting their meals. They lay so still that a big toad, crawling towards the pond, did not see them. He thought they were part of the bank of the pond.

But the grass-snake saw him. As the slow toad passed by, the snake slid back his head a little and then struck. The toad saw the snake's head coming and in a trice he poured out an evil-smelling liquid over his warty back. The snake tasted this when the toad was in his mouth and in disgust dropped his prey hurriedly. The toad lay still for a moment and then began to crawl away.

The snake lowered its head again and struck once more, for he could not bear to see the toad escaping. But once again the evil taste forced him to drop the toad, and this time the slow-crawling creature managed to reach the pond, drop into the water, and swim swiftly to safety.

'Did you see that?' cried the watching blackbird. 'The toad escaped. I saw him, I saw him!'

'That toad tasted horrible,' said the grass-snake to the adder.

'I must eat something else to get the taste out of my mouth.'

'I have known you to smell even worse than that toad tasted!' said the adder, uncoiling himself to stare at his companion. 'Do you remember the time that a man caught you and was going to kill you? You made yourself smell so horrible that he dropped you and you took the chance to escape.'

'That man thought I was you,' said the grass-snake, indignantly. 'I cannot defend myself as you can. I have no poison fangs so the only thing I could do was to make myself disgusting. I am always suffering because I am mistaken for you. I wish you would go away and never come near me.'

'I will very soon,' said the adder. 'But first I must change my skin! It has already split round my mouth and is most uncomfortable.'

The grass-snake watched him. The adder rubbed his head against a stone to loosen his skin. Then, very gradually, the whole of his scaly skin peeled off, and the adder was able to glide out of it, leaving it turned inside out like a stocking!

'I shall go to find a wife now that I am so handsome,' he called to the grass-snake, as he glided off.

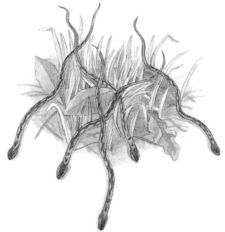

'Where will she lay her eggs?' called the grass-snake after him. 'I shall put mine in that heap of manure at the end of the field, so do not have yours laid there!'

'We do not lay eggs!' called the adder, scornfully. 'Our young ones come from the eggs as they are dropped by the mother adder. Didn't you know that?'

The grass-snake made no answer. He glided away swiftly, and the blackbird cried out the glad news.

'The woodland is safe! The snakes are gone! All clear, friends, all clear!'

THE END

OAK TREE GUESTS

THE oak-tree that spread its branches over the hedgerow knew almost *every* bird of the countryside. It knew the starlings, who often sat in dozens among the leaves, chattering at the tops of their queer little voices. It knew the thrushes and the blackbirds and heard them singing at dawn. The little red robins were its friends, and the noisy sparrows, with their cry of 'Phillip, Phillip!' It knew the feel of countless little feet, clinging closely to the twigs. It had felt the thrush wiping its beak after a feast on the berries in the hedge below. It had sheltered the close-hidden nests of all kinds of birds and had been the first home of many youngsters.

The tree heard the skylark singing in the early mornings, but it did not know the brown bird very well, for the lark liked to run on the ground and seldom perched in a tree. Neither did the tree know the peewits for their wild cry, 'Poo-wee, poo-wee!' as they circled in their hundreds over the fields – for the peewits never came to the oak-tree, preferring the open fields.

The oak had other friends besides birds. It liked to feel the squirrels scampering about the branches and the touch of the dormouse's tiny feet, when it ran up the trunk to look for acorns. It was a wise old tree, always beautiful, whatever the season of the year. In spring its leaves were pale green and tender; in summer it stood clothed in glossy dark green and its shade was welcome to the creatures of the hedgerow; when autumn came it turned a pale, russet brown, and all through the winter it stretched out strong bare branches to the sky, with a few brown leaves still rattling in the wind.

Now it was winter and the branches were bare and cold. The wind whistled through them and the birds no longer roosted there at night, but found a cosy place in the thick green ivy below. But in the daytime the oak-tree had many guests.

Some came for the acorns, a few of which still stood stiffly in their pipe-like holders on the twigs. Some came for the spiders and grubs that lay hidden in the crannies of the rough bark. The oak-tree was glad to see its guests, for many of the beetle-grubs were its enemies and would damage the old tree with their boring, if the birds did not search for them and eat them.

One December day, when the wind blew cold, a sturdy slate-grey and chestnut bird flew over the hedgerow. It whistled cheerfully, like a schoolboy – 'Tui, tui, tui!' The oak-tree knew that call well, for it had heard it all through the spring. The nuthatch had nested in the tree then and had brought up its young ones there.

24

There was a hole in the trunk of the oak-tree and the nuthatch had put dead leaves and grass into it, making a cosy nest for the eggs. The hole had been rather too big, so the clever bird had brought clay and blocked up the entrance until it was the right size.

One day another little bird had come and peeped in the hole – a small brown bird, silvery white underneath.

It was a tree-creeper, looking for a place for its nest. It had pulled at a piece of loose bark and wondered if it should stuff moss and grass behind it for a nest. But then the nuthatch had come rushing out of its hole and frightened it away – so it had nested in another tree, behind an ivy-stem, not very far away.

Another day a spotted woodpecker had come and with his strong beak had drummed on the bark of the oak-tree. The noise had disturbed

the young nuthatches, and the mother bird had come to the entrance of the nest-hole to see what was the matter.

'What are you doing?' she had cried, shrilly. 'You cannot nest in this tree. It is ours!'

25

'I am looking for an old half-dead tree,' the woodpecker had said, drumming again on the bark. 'I don't like to build my nest in a healthy tree – it is so difficult to drill a hole in the wood for a nest. But it is easy to peck out dead wood and make a hole deep down in the trunk.'

'This tree is no use to you,' the nuthatch had replied, sharply, 'It is an old tree, but alive and strong. You will find no dead wood in it. Go away, you disturb us with your loud drumming. There is an old pine on the hill that was struck with lightning last autumn – a big branch of it is dead and you could easily drill a nest-hole there.'

The woodpecker had flown off, and the nuthatch had heard him drumming on the pine, half a mile away. It was a fine place for a nest, and the woodpecker had soon made a hole there. Five small woodpeckers had hatched out of the creamy white eggs, and were quite happy and comfortable on the wood chips that served them for a nest at the bottom of the hole.

Now all the youngsters of the woodpecker, the treecreeper and the nuthatch had flown away, and were seeking their fortunes in the country-side round about. The days were cold and frosty and food was not easy to find. The old woodpecker was wily and knew the best trees for hunting – and that was how he remembered the oak-tree on this cold winter's day.

He flew off to it, his gay plumage showing up brightly in the winter sunshine. His wings were barred with black and white, he had bright patches of white on his shoulders, and gay splashes of crimson on the nape of his neck and under his body near his tail.

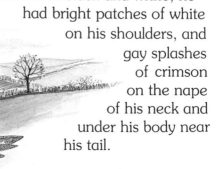

He came to the oak-tree and perched on the trunk, two toes in front and two behind so that he might climb easily. His stiff tail feathers helped to support him, and his strong beak sounded the furrowed bark. 'R-r-r-r-r-r!'

He began to look for insects and spiders in the crevices of the bark. The small ones he took out with his long sticky tongue, the large ones he found by tapping and loosening the bark. He worked upwards and to the right – and just as he was going to pass under a branch he met another bird, much smaller than himself, also looking for insects in the trunk! Each was frightened and flew to a branch above. They looked at one another.

The second bird was the little brown tree-creeper. He had a long curved beak and bright eyes. He spoke humbly to the woodpecker.

'May I look for food in your tree?' he asked. There are plenty of cocoons under the bark, and I have found some grubs too.'

'It is not my tree,' said the woodpecker. 'I did not nest here. But I don't want to share with you, tree-creeper. Find somewhere else to feed.'

The tree-creeper's sharp eyes saw a curled-up woodlouse in a cranny. He inserted his long curved beak behind the bark and pulled out the insect. The woodpecker watched him angrily, and fluffed out his feathers in rage.

'Quet, quet, quet, quet!' he cried, and was just going to rush at the tree-creeper when heard a loud whistle from the top of the

tree. Both birds looked up. It was the nuthatch, just arrived to look for any remaining acorns, or maybe a hazel-nut or two from the hedge below.

'This is my tree!' cried the nuthatch and whistled again. 'Tui, tui, tui! This is my tree! I had my nest here. This is my tree! Go away, woodpecker and tree-creeper.'

The birds below looked up at the nuthatch. He was slate-grey above and chestnut below and through his eyes ran a stripe. The woodpecker did not move, but the tree-creeper was frightened and slipped underneath a branch, hanging there, with his head downwards.

'You and I eat different food,' said the woodpecker to the nuthatch. 'We can feast on the same tree without interfering with one another. See, nuthatch, there are two hazel-nuts in the ditch below, fallen from the hedge. Take them before the mice find them.'

The nuthutch cocked his head on one side and looked into the ditch. He saw the nuts and flew down. He picked one up in his beak and flew back to the oak-tree with it. The woodpecker watched to see what he would do. How could he eat such a hard, woody thing?

The nuthatch was clever. He found a place in the bark of the trunk where he could press in the hazelnut so that it stayed there, gripped by the ridges of the bark. Then he held firmly on to the trunk with his strong feet and began to hammer at the nutshell with his big beak. 'Tap-tap-tap! Tap-tap-tap!' He hammered at the nut until the shell broke. Then he quickly pecked out the kernel inside and swallowed it. That was his way of dealing with nuts!

He spied an acorn hanging on the oak-tree. He pecked it off, crying. 'Tui, tui, tui! I tell you this is my tree! Get away!'

The tree-creeper cried out in fright, and the woodpecker drummed in excitement on the trunk. Two jays, flying over from the wood, heard the noise and swooped down to see what it was about. One of them snatched the acorn from the nuthatch and the other screeched harshly, 'Kraak, kraak, kraak! There are some acorns left. Let us have them!'

Off flew the tree-creeper, the woodpecker and the nuthatch, terrified of the big, screaming birds. 'It's a pity we quarrelled!' whistled the nuthatch. 'There was enough food for all of us, really! Meet me there to-morrow. Tui, tui, tui!'

THE END

THE SPINNER
IN THE HEDGE

IT was a warm and sunny November day. After a few cold nights, which had sent hundreds of leaves fluttering from the trees onto the ground below, there had come a warm spell. To-day the sky was blue and only a few wispy clouds were to be seen.

The trees gleamed yellow, pink and red. They still had some leaves left on them and beneath them bright crimson blackberry sprays that waved high in the air, a few golden hazel-leaves and some red and yellow hawthorn-leaves. The ivy was green and thick. It did not drop its leaves in the autumn, but shed a few all the year round. There were still flies buzzing about late blossoms in the hedgerows, and a big queen wasp that had been tempted out by the sunshine. It was warm in the shelter of the blackberry bush, so warm that a little colony of sparrows had stopped to preen their feathers there.

A big spider was watching the birds carefully. It was an old and wise spider. It knew the unexpected ways of toads, who could

shoot out a tongue and snap up fly or spider. It had seen the cleverness of the swallows that could catch any insect that flew. The spider was not very much afraid of the sparrows. She had often watched their clumsiness when they tried to catch an insect on the wing. She knew she could dart away and hide if one of the little brown birds saw her.

What she was worrying about was her web. She had made a fine web the night before, for she had guessed that the day would be warm and that there might be flies about. She was hungry and wanted a good meal.

Now the sparrows were sitting in a heap near the web. If one of them fluttered his wings, the web would break and all the spider's work would be wasted. And then, even as she watched, it happened. Two sparrows began to fight, and one of them fell. Straight through the fine, silky web he tumbled, and the spider, angry and frightened, ran through the bush to get away from the noise and the scuffling.

Suddenly the sparrows spread their wings and flew away – all but one. He decided to stay where he was. It was warm and sunny in the bush, he was very full of seeds and he didn't want to move. He flew to the top of a blackberry-spray and perched there in the sunshine.

The spider was just about to climb up the very same spray. She had made up her mind to make a new web there, stretched from that spray to another near by. She had noticed that a great many flies seemed to fly over the hedgerow just there.

She made an angry noise when the small sparrow perched and swung on her spray. The sparrow heard it and saw her.

'What's the matter?' he asked in surprise. 'Why do you glare at me like that with all your eight eyes? Don't be afraid of me – I shan't eat you to-day. I've just had a fine feast of seeds from the hayrick.'

'You are perching on the spray I wanted for my web,' said the spider, glowering. 'Can't you move?'

'Yes, if you'll let me see you making your web,' said the sparrow, who was still young enough to like watching things. He hopped to another spray.

The spider took a good look at the young sparrow and as he really did seem very small and fat, she thought it would be safe to get on with her web. So she began.

'It's easy,' she said. 'Any spider knows how to spin. I have little knobs underneath me. They are my spinnerets and from them comes the thread for my webs. I can make it sticky or not, as I like.'

The sparrow watched the spider make four threads, two at the bottom and two at the sides of the blackberry-sprays. Then he watched her go to the middle of the top thread and drop to the middle of the bottom thread, leaving a new thread behind her. She climbed half-way up this thread, and then began to travel up and down from the middle thread to the outside threads, making the spokes of her web as she went.

When all the spokes were finished the spider went back to the middle again, and began to make the spiral thread that wound round and round the spokes until she reached the outside threads. Then back went the spider to the middle again, weaving another spiral thread. But as she went, she ate up the first spiral!

The sparrow was astonished. What a waste of work! Then he noticed that the second spiral was hung with sticky drops.

'Why do you put those drops there?' he asked. 'They look sticky.'

'Of course they are sticky!' said the spider, scornfully. 'When a fly comes by, it flies into the web and gets caught on the stickiness.'

'But why don't you get caught in your own web?' asked the sparrow, surprised.

'Because I am sensible enough to keep my legs well oiled,'

answered the spider. 'If I didn't oil them well, I should stick to my own web. Look at the ends of my feet – do you see my comb-like claws? I can hold easily to the thin threads of my web with those claws. Now I am going to hide under this leaf and see if I can catch a fly in my web. There is nothing more for you to see, so you can go. I don't want you to break my web with your clumsy feet.'

But the young sparrow didn't go. He stayed there, watching. Soon a small fly came hurrying by, anxious to get to the ivy blossom it could smell.   It didn't see the web and flew straight into it.   The spider felt the web shaking, and rushed down from her leaf. She plunged her jaws into the struggling fly and paralysed it. Then she sucked its blood. Back she went to her hiding place and waited patiently.

Almost at once a big bluebottle buzzed by. He saw the sparrow and turned back in fear, only to catch his wings in the web. At once the waiting spider hurried down again – but when she saw the big fly she paused.

Then quickly she made up her mind what to do. She ran to where he was struggling and began to cut the web here and there. At last she had cut all the threads but one that held the fly. Then she began to twirl the insect round and round on the one thread, and as she spun him round, she let out another thread that bound him more and more closely. Then, when he was quite harmless, she ran down to him and killed him.

The watching sparrow began to feel quite afraid of the clever spinner. He was glad he was too big for her to weave a web around him.

Then there came a loud droning sound and a queen wasp sailed by. She flew right into the middle of the web, and in her struggles she became wrapped round and round with it.

'Let me out,' she buzzed, angrily. 'Let me out. If you don't let me out I shall sting you to death.'

The spider ran in alarm to her leaf and hid there. But the big queen wasp buzzed even more loudly.

She struggled so fiercely that the spider was frightened. She ran out and began to cut the threads that bound the wasp. When she had cut them all, the wasp dropped down onto the woodland floor. She began to clean the web from her body. The spider, afraid that she would come back, hid herself under a leaf, trembling.

The sparrow called to the spider.

'She's gone! But your web is spoilt,' he said. 'Come and make another one.'

'No,' said the spider. 'I am tired. Besides, I believe the frost is coming, and then there will be no flies to catch. I shall find a cranny in the bark of the oak-tree and hide there for the winter. I like the oak-tree. I laid my eggs there. Did you see them? I put them in a yellow cocoon of silk. They hatched out, and in October the tiny spiders all went adventuring through the fields on long threads of gossamer. I watched them go. I was glad to see them leave the oak-tree, because I did not want them to stay and catch my flies.'

'Yes, I saw the young spiders,' said the sparrow, spreading his wings to fly. 'I ate some. Perhaps one day I shall come back and eat you.'

He flew away. The spider ran up the trunk of the oak-tree, and very soon hid herself under a rough piece of bark. She huddled there, looking shrivelled and dead. But she was only pretending! She could come alive in a twinkling if she wanted to!

THE END

BUSHY TALES

ALL through January the weather had been cold and frosty. The wind had blown from the east, and how the woodland creatures hated an east wind! It stung their bright eyes, it pinched their sensitive noses and pierced right through thick fur or fluffy feathers. Those that had warm hiding-places, holes lined with moss and dead leaves, huddled there, silent, waiting patiently for a change in the weather outside.

The big oak-tree waited patiently, too. It had slept during the cold days, for there had been no work to do. The leaves that had worked so hard in the summertime had all dropped down to the ditch below, except for a few that still hung here and there. The oak-tree was waiting – waiting for the sap to rise, so that its buds could swell and open; but the time had not come yet.

When February came in the weather softened and the wind swung round to the west. A warmth crept over the fields, the hedgehog unrolled himself and took a stroll. And deep in the heart of the oak-tree someone woke up!

Who was it sleeping there? It was a red squirrel, with his bushy tail curled right round him for a blanket. There was a curious hollow half-way up the oak-tree just where the first big branch joined the trunk. It had slowly formed there after a great storm one night when the oak-tree had been struck by lightning. No great damage had been done, but in that one place the wood had rotted little by little and at last there came a hollow place, made bigger each year by the peckings and scrapings of many woodland creatures.

The red squirrel had built a nest there, far back in the spring-time. And in it he had brought up his pretty little family of six young squirrels. The mice had watched him tearing up grass with his front paws, to make bedding for the little ones. They had often gone to peep at the nest, too, for it was a good one, made of all kinds of things. The squirrel had stripped bark off young trees, he had brought twigs and woven them together with the bark and he stuffed up all the crevices and cracks with moss and leaves. Sometimes, on a very rainy day, 'the rain had run into the hollow where the nest was, but it was quite waterproof. The squirrel was a good craftsman and not a drop of water came through the nest to chill the young ones.

All the woodland creatures had known the squirrel and his wife very well indeed. They were such a lively, merry pair! They had scampered up and down the trees, using their long, sharp claws to dig into the bark as they went. They had chattered to one another. They had nibbled at toadstools to see which they liked and when they found those that had a nutty taste they had become most excited and had called loudly to one another. They had often gone to the next field, too, where there was a chestnut-tree, and had eaten the flowerbuds; and as for the wild cherries, there was no hope of anyone else feasting on those once the squirrels had found the tree!

The oak-tree liked the squirrels. It liked to feel their pattering feet, even when the bark was scraped and scored by their sharp claws. It was delighted when a big nest was built in its hollow. Here the young squirrels were born and grew up lively and mischievous.

One day the mother squirrel went off to the pine wood to get some cones and did not come back. The stoat ran to the oak-tree the same night and called to the squirrel who was left. 'Your mate has been caught in a trap. The keeper has her now and she is nailed to his door. He says she spoilt some of his young trees in the spring.'

The squirrel was full of sadness. He sat and moped in the tree and the young ones, seeing that he took no notice of them, ran off into the branches. Then, very daring, they scampered down to the hedge and leapt over the field to the pine wood they could see in the distance. That was the last that the squirrel saw of them, and he soon forgot them. He forgot his sadness, too, after a few days and ran about as lively as ever. The woodland creatures have short memories, and no one is sad for long.

When the autumn came he was very busy. He pulled the hazel-nuts from the hedge. Some he had eaten, but most he hid away. 'I shall need these when I wake up now and again in the cold weather,' he thought. 'I will hide some of them so that I can feast when I am ready.'

Some he hid under the dead leaves. Others he pushed into a little cranny under the roots of the ivy. Yet another store he hid under a stone. When the acorns fell from the oak-tree he hid those, too. Often these sprouted and grew into tiny oak-trees, and that puzzled the squirrel very much.

All through the cold month of January, the little, red squirrel slept, warmly and cosily. When the east wind tried to get into his nest he merely wrapped himself more closely in his tail. Then came the day when the west wind blew warmly and moistly, and the squirrel awoke and stretched himself. His bright black eyes and tufted ears appeared as he looked out of the oak tree. No snow! No frost! Sunshine and warmth!

Just then, the robin who lived in the hedgerow hopped up beside him. The redbreast was a gossip. He always knew everything and heard everything. The squirrel looked at him and wondered why he seemed so excited. 'To-day I saw a strange thing,' began the robin. 'I saw a squirrel like you, but dressed all in grey instead of red.'

'I don't believe you,' said the red squirrel, yawning and stretching out his feet.

'Believe me or not, it's true,' said the robin, with a loud trill.

'Ask the rabbits. They saw him, too. And he said he was going to turn you out of this tree and have it for himself. A good thing, too, if you do go, red squirrel, for I haven't forgotten how you once took my day-old nestlings and ate them!'

'Go away,' said the squirrel, crossly. 'You are a scold. I don't often take eggs or young birds and you know that I shall . . .'

But the red squirrel did not finish what he was saying. He had seen something strange, and he sat staring in wonder at it. The robin had spoken the truth. There was another squirrel, and he was grey, not red. He came scampering up the oak-tree and looked impudently at the red squirrel.

'Good-day, cousin,' he said. 'The robin told me you were asleep, but I see you are now awake.'

'Where do you come from?' asked the red squirrel in astonishment. 'I have never seen a squirrel like you before. All my family are red.'

'I am an American squirrel,' said the grey visitor, looking at the red squirrel with large, bright eyes. 'My great-great-grandparents were brought to a big zoo in London with many other grey squirrels. Some of them were set free and played about the parks in London Town. We like your country so much that we think we will live here and make it our own. So I and many others are finding good places in the country-side to live, and this year we've come as far as this wood.'

The red squirrel listened in anger. He leapt to a branch above the grey squirrel, sat up on his hind legs and made fierce little barking noises.

'How dare you take our country-side for your own?' he chattered, angrily. 'How dare you? It is ours. We have lived here for hundreds of years, we have hidden our nuts round about every autumn, we know all the hollow trees, all the best nesting-places, and all the little folk of the country-side. We belong here!'

'Well, we grey squirrels must live somewhere,' said the other squirrel, fluffing out his bushy tail.

'Live in the towns, then,' said the red squirrel, 'and leave the country-side to us.'

'No, no,' said the other. 'We like nuts and acorns, beech-mast and toadstools as much as you do. We shall live in the woods wherever we please and eat what we like. And you red squirrels must go! There is not room in one place for both grey and red squirrels. We are stronger and fiercer than you, so you must go.'

'What, leave this hedgerow I know so well! Leave all the friends I have? Never!' cried the red squirrel and leapt down the tree in a fury.

He was angry and he was hungry and when when he reached the hedgerow he remembered that he had hidden some nuts somewhere. At first he could not remember where, but soon it came into his mind that he had put a little store in the cranny under the ivy-roots. He leapt over there and put in his small paw. No nuts!

'Ho ho, I found those!' cried the watching grey squirrel. 'And a good hiding-place, too!'

The red squirrel chattered angrily and ran to the stone under which he had hidden other nuts. None there either! 'I took those, too!' called the grey squirrel, frisking about in delight.

'And I took a few you hid under the dead leaves!' squeaked a small mouse, peeping out of a hole. 'But there are still a few nuts tucked away at the bottom of the oak-tree, red squirrel, if you are hungry.'

But before the red squirrel could get there, the grey one bounded down the trunk and took all the nuts himself! The red squirrel shrank back, half afraid and then, seeing two more grey squirrels coming scampering down from the alder-trees near by, he suddenly shot up the oak-tree and went back to his nest. He was frightened and sad.

'I must go,' he thought. 'I cannot live with these bold robbers. I am too shy, too timid. I am afraid of them. I must leave this woodland and go far away, where grey squirrels are unheard of . . . and yet maybe they will follow me there and soon there will be nowhere for us to go!'

That night the red squirrel crept out of his nest. It was bright moonlight and the air was warm. The owl and the stoat were out, but the squirrel feared neither of them. Softly and silently he slipped down the oak-tree for the last time and called good-bye to the tiny mouse at the foot. Soon he was gone, a little dark shadow in the moonlight. None of the woodland folk ever knew where he went, none ever heard of him again; but they missed the lively little creature with his chestnut coat.

The grey squirrels stayed. They used the old nest in the oak-tree; they used all the old hiding-places. They are about the woodland still, merry and bold – but the little red squirrel is miles away and will never come back.

THE END

THE BUMBLE-BEE
HUMS

ALL the woodland folk liked to hear the humming of the bees. It was a summery sound, lazy and warm. The earliest bees had been out in March, seeking for the flowers that opened on the bank below. More bees had come in April, and very soon there had been heard the loud booming of the big brown and yellow bumble-bee. Zoooooooom! Zoooooooom! It was a lovely droning sound, never heard in the cold days of winter.

The bumble-bee had slept all through the winter in a little hole on the north side of the hedgerow-bank. It was a cold hole, especially when the north winds blew in January and February. But the bumble-bee had chosen it carefully. She knew that to choose a warm hole on the south side of the hedge would be dangerous. The sun came early to the south bank, and sent its warm beams into every nook and cranny there, waking up all the small sleepers. But to wake up on a sunny day in February and crawl out might mean death when the frost returned at night. It

44

was better to sleep in a cold place and not to wake until all fear of frosts was past.

The bumble-bee had carefully made a honey-pot for herself before going to sleep. Then, if by chance she should awake, she could have a sip of honey from her pot and need not run the risk of leaving her hole. The hole was small. It had been made by an earthworm and the bee squatted down in the enlarged room at the end of the hole, her honey-pot beside her. She did not wake until February and then, although the sun was shining warmly on the south side of the hedge, her hole was still rimmed around by frost and she did not stir out. She sipped her honey and went to sleep again.

At last, on a warm spring day, she walked out, feeling rather top-heavy and a little dazed with her long, cold sleep. She spread her wings and the woodland heard once again her loud booming hum. The warm days must be coming if the bumble-bee was about!

The bee decided to look for a new hole. It would be a warm one this time and a bigger one.

There was one rather big hole on the sunny side of a bank, but the bumble-bee came out quickly after one look, for a most enormous spider lived there! She looked under an old stone and saw a fat toad peering at her with gleaming eyes. He knew she was dangerous and did not flick out his tongue to eat her. But she backed out quickly. Then she flew to another part of the bank, humming busily. And at last she found exactly the right hole!

It had been made by mice, and their smell still hung about the little hole. The bumble-bee altered the hole to her liking and then fetched in some moss. She crawled out again and brought back some grass. Then she visited some flowers and returned with pollen which she packed into the hole. She looked at the heap of moss, grass and pollen, and decided to lay her eggs.

So she built some egg cells and put pollen into each. Then she laid her eggs, one in each cell, white, long-shaped eggs which she spread herself over. Beside her were several of her honey-pots, full of honey. Soon her eggs hatched out into grubs – but how hungry they were! They ate up all the pollen in their cells, and the bumble-bee bit a tiny hole in each cell and passed more food through to her growing children.

Now the big bumble-bee was busy all day long. She went out to find food for her first batch of children; she laid more eggs; she built more and more cells and taught the first batch of young bees how to help her.

One morning, she heard the loud humming of another creature near by and she stopped in her flight to see who it was. It was a large queen-wasp, and she was doing exactly what the bumble-bee herself had done some weeks before. She was hunting for a hole in the bank!

'You are late in finding a home,' boomed the big bumble-bee.

'I only wake when the sun has plenty of warmth in it,' buzzed the wasp. 'All winter I slept in a hidden cranny behind an ivy-root in the hedge. A little mouse woke me up once when he came hunting for the nuts the squirrel hid, but of course he soon fled when he saw me!'

'I have a fine nest in an old mouse-hole,' hummed the bee, settling down beside the big queen-wasp. 'Come and see it.'

But the wasp was in a hurry. Summer would soon be here and she must lay her eggs. She ran to a hole and crawled inside to see if it would suit her. But a big beetle was there, and showed her his great, ugly jaws. The wasp hurried out again and flew to another hole. This was too big, and full of rubbish.

At last she found exactly what she needed. This was an old tunnel made by the mole the summer before. Part of the roof had fallen in at the back. The wasp walked all over the hole, touching the walls with her feelers. This was a good place. She was pleased with it. She crawled up to the roof and there she found the root of a hawthorn-bush jutting out. She could hang her nest from that.

She left the hole and flew up into the air, circling as she did so, noticing everything around her hole: the stone near by, the tuft of grass, the thistle. . . all these things would help her to know her hole again. Then she flew higher still into the air, and noticed bigger things: the near-by ditch, the beech tree, the big bramble-spray that waved high in the air. She would know her way back again now!

The queen-wasp was going to build a city and be its ruler. She was going to have thousands of subjects, who would work for her night and day. She was ready to begin, for the warm sun had heated her blood and given her strength.

She flew off to the common up on the hill, and looked about her as she went. She was hunting for a piece of oak from which she could take a scraping to start her city. She found a gate-post and settled down on it. She bit a piece of wood out, a mere shaving, with her strong jaws. She chewed it and chewed it until it was paper-pulp. Then back she flew to the hole she had taken for her own. She crawled in – and immediately began a fierce buzzing, for there were three ants there! She drove her sting into each one and threw them out of the hole, little curled-up brown things, poisoned by her sting.

She stuck the paper pellet to the root at the top of the hole and then went off for more. In and out she flew all day long, building the roof of her house first, for wasps live in upside-down homes! Every time she left the hole she carried with her a pellet of earth, to give her plenty of room for her city.

She often met the big bumble-bee, who told her that she herself had now plenty of workers to help her, for many of her grubs had grown into bees, and did her work.

'Come with me for a while,' said the bumble-bee. 'The fields are full of flowers.'

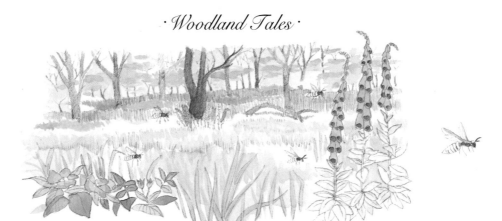

'I have no use for flowers,' said the wasp, impatiently. 'Leave me, cousin. I am too busy. I have many things to do, and as yet I have no helpers as you have!'

Soon there was a pile of earth outside the old mole-hole and inside, built safely under an umbrella-like covering of grey paper, were many wasp-cells, each containing a small grub. They hung head downwards in their cells and were tightly glued to the top so that they could not fall out of the hole at the bottom. Soon they grew large and fat and were so wedged in that they could not fall.

Then each grub spun a silk sheet over the cell-opening and formed a cocoon. The queen-wasp waited for them to come forth from their cells and at last the time came. Each little wasp bit through its cell and came out. They cleaned themselves up and then looked round the nest.

Very soon they were helping the queen-wasp, their mother, to do the tasks she had done alone for some weeks .

They helped to feed the new grubs. They cleaned the nest. And then one morning, when the sun came right into the hole, the young wasps went to the opening and looked out. They spread their shining wings and flew into the air, each small wasp taking careful notice of all the things around their hole so that they would know the way back and would not get lost. Then off they went, all knowing exactly what to do, although they had never done their new tasks before.

Some of them found the old oak post from which their mother had scraped shavings to make the paper-pulp she used in building her city. They too took scrapings and chewed them into pulp, taking the pellets home again to build on to their nest, which was now three stories high.

Other wasps went to a sunny wall on which many flies crawled. They caught the flies, cut off their wings, heads and legs, and carried them back to the nest to feed the young grubs. One wasp found a hiding-place in which four moths crouched, and, cutting off their wings, carried the bodies away for food.

They had their enemies, and so had the young bumble-bees. The spotted fly-catcher had come back from its winter haunts and darted at the passing bees and wasps, as well as the flies. The great tit, too, would sometimes wait outside the hole where the bumble-bee had her nest and would pounce on an unwary bee just leaving.

One day all the bees and wasps heard a strange noise. It was a high humming, very shrill and loud, like a wasp or bee army on the march. Every wasp and every bumble-bee flew to see what it was. And they saw a strange sight! A great cloud of honey-bees was coming over the field towards the wood. It was led by the queen-bee and thousands of bees were following her. The queen-wasp flew near and demanded to know what had happened.

'We come from a hive far away,' boomed the queen-honey-bee. 'I had so many worker bees that the hive became too small. So I have brought half the hive away with me and I am looking for a new home. I have left behind me some princesses in the hive. One of them will become queen in my place.'

'We do not swarm!' said the queen-wasp. 'I make my city as big as I want it.'

'You are only a wasp!' buzzed the honey-bee. 'Your city will crumble to nothing in the autumn and all your people will die! But my people will live with me, for we store up honey for the cold days!'

The wasp flew off to her hole. The bee swarm settled on the lowest branch of the oak-tree, and then in a short while flew off again, no one knew where.

'Zoooooooom!' buzzed the bumble-bee to the queen-wasp. 'Who would be a hive-bee and live in slavery? Not I! Zoooooooom!'

THE END

THE
WHISTLER

IN the lovely month of May the woodland was beautiful to see. The leaves of the trees were a brilliant green, the brambles threw graceful branches into the air, full of tender young leaves and the ivy shone dark and glossy. When the May blossom came it lay among the tree trunks like drifts of summer snow and its fragrance brought a myriad bees, moths, butterflies and other insects to it.

The oak-tree at the edge of the wood was now full of leaf. It was the last of all the trees to put out its tender, feather-shaped leaves and the birds whose nests were among its branches were glad of their shelter. They liked the soft, green light that the leaves made and they liked to see them waving in the wind. It was good to have a nest in the oak-tree in May.

On the bank there were many flowers, enjoying the hot sun. The cow-parsley foamed there and in the wet ditch great clumps of golden king-cups raised their heads to the sun. Lilac milkmaids, the pretty cuckoo-flower, grew in the field and danced

all day long. Buttercups made a carpet of gold and red clover
raised its sweet head to the humming bees. All day long the
cuckoo called. It was a summer sound and the woodland folk
liked it.

At sunset, when the buttercups glowed even more golden, and
the shadow of the oak-tree was so long that it stretched half-way
across the field, a strange sound was heard. It was a clear, low
whistle, rather bird-like. It came from the pond that lay not far
from the oak-tree. The hedgerow folk heard it, and knew what it
was.

It was the otter whistling to his mate. She lived in the pond, for
it was very deep in places and big fish could be found there. It
had once been part of a stream that had run into the river not far
away. But the stream had changed its course so that it emptied
into the river at a different place. And now the big pond was all
that was left of the old part of the stream.

In the old days many otters had swum in the pond when it had
been part of the stream and even now, when it was only a pond,

they came to it, travelling over the fields. Around it were the alder-trees they loved, and beneath the roots of the alders were fine hiding-places, holes where an otter could rest in peace. It was a good pond.

In the autumn before, two otters had come to the pond. The woodland folk knew them well, both in the water and out. The birds knew least about them, for the otters were night-time creatures, and most birds sleep through the night. But the owl knew them best and sometimes hooted when he heard the otters whistling to one another.

The otters were dusky-brown creatures covered with dense fur, so thick that not a drop of water could wet their warm bodies.

They were large creatures, over a metre long. The inquisitive hedgehog often sniffed at the 'spur' or footprint left by the otters in the mud at the side of the pond. These prints showed the otters to have rounded toes, webbed for swimming, for they were marvellous swimmers.

Sometimes, at sunset, the late robin could see two flat black heads moving about on the pond surface. He watched the otters swimming and playing, rolling their oily bodies round in a circle, as clever as fish in the water. They swam with their front paws only, and used their flattened tails as rudders. It was wonderful to watch them.

The alder-trees knew the otters very well indeed, for the animals had made their nursery under their roots. The alders sighed in the wind and remembered. The mother otter had found the big hole one day and had whistled to her mate to come and look. To get to the hole under the roots they had to dive right into the water, and then scramble into the underground chamber as best they could. The hole led upwards, criss-crossed by alder-roots. At its top end it was dry and roomy.

'This will do for our nursery,' said the otter to her mate. 'No one will find us here. There will be plenty of room for all of us when the babies come. I shall bring rushes and grass here and the purple flowers of the great reed. And I shall make a soft nest.'

And that winter, during a warm spell, the mother otter laid her three little ones there in the big, dark hole under the alders. They were quite blind, but they were already covered with warm, downy fur. The mother was very proud of them and licked them all over. So did the father. They smelt sweet and were so warm and playful.

'You must hunt for us,' said the mother to her mate. 'It is cold to-night, and I must not leave these little ones to get chilled. Go and bring us some fish. I am hungry.'

The big otter slid into the water. He closed his short, rounded ears all the time he was under the surface, so that no water should get into them. He went to the deepest part of the pond, where he knew there were big fish and very soon chased and caught one. Back he went to the hole.

   The mother otter bit a large piece out of the fish's shoulder, and then ate the fish all the way down to the tail. This she left, for in the otter family it is not good manners to eat the tail. The tiny otters sniffed and snickered round the little bits of fish the mother had left. The smell excited them.

   The alder-trees often felt the little otters scrambling about over their roots and they liked it. And then one evening, when the sun had just gone down, leaving a golden glow in the western sky, the mother otter took her young into the pond for the first time. They had often been to the edge of the water that lapped into their dark hole. One of them had even slipped into it and been pulled out by its mother, who scolded it and bit it sharply for a punishment. But this was the first time they had ever been out into the great world beyond their small, dark home underneath the alder-roots.

'Come !'
said the otter
to her three young
ones. She slid into the water
and one by one the three small
otters followed her. They did not feel
the chill of the water, for by now they had
thick, dense, fur coats – two coats, really, one
of short fur and one of longer hairs.

At first they floundered about, not at all sure what to do in the water, but their mother was patient. She took them quickly up to the surface. Then she showed them how to swim properly.

'Use your tail to guide you,' she said. 'Use your front paws for swimming. Let your back paws drag loose.'

The young otters were clumsy at first, but they enjoyed the adventure. They watched their mother and father swim gracefully here and there, turning and tumbling easily through the water. They gazed in amazement as they saw a large fish chased and caught and they snickered together in terror when they spied their mother chasing a startled moor-hen, which took to its wings and escaped just in time!

All through the spring-time the young otters learnt many things from their parents. They learnt how to turn over big stones to hunt for crayfish. They found out how to twist and turn swiftly in the water to catch a darting fish. They went on land

and found that they could run easily on their four, webbed feet. They caught frogs for themselves and grew fat and strong.

One night the father otter whistled good-bye to his mate. 'The youngsters are big now,' he said. 'I am going away to the sea.' 'Why is that?' asked his mate.

'This pond is drying up a little,' answered the otter. 'I am afraid that it may disappear altogether if the summer is hot. Even the river near by may dry up, and as I count on the current to take me down to the sea, I shall go while there is plenty of time. I shall spend the summer in an old sea-cave I know, where many bats live. In the autumn I will come back to you.'

The big otter swam to the edge of the pond, shook the water

from his thick coat like
a dog and disappeared in the long grass. He had gone to the river. The robin, who loved the long twilight evenings of Maytime, followed him, flitting along in the bushes beside him. She saw him enter the swiftly flowing river and, with front paws pressed under his chin, float gently down with the current.

His mate missed him sadly. The hedgerow folk often heard her whistling for him on these warm May evenings, when the sunset glow lasted for a long time in the western skies. She wanted him to see how well their cubs had grown, she wanted him to swim and play with her on these sweet, warm nights. But he had gone.

The weather grew hotter. The pond, never very full since a hot summer two years since, grew lower. The mother otter found that her underground chamber was now hardly under water. It would soon no longer be a safe hiding-place. She hunted round the pond for another. But there was none big enough for four fully grown otters.

'We must part,' said the mother to her young ones. 'You are old enough to go your own way now. You can fish and swim, dive and walk for miles on the land. You know how to avoid traps. I have taken you to the river and shown you how to let the current carry you along. You have often found holes big enough to hide in. Now the time has come for you to work and hunt for yourselves.'

'But where will you go?' asked the smallest of the three.

'I may go down to the sea, too, as your father did,' said the otter. 'There are many things to eat there that we do not not find inland.'

'Are there fish there?' asked the biggest otter, hungrily.

'Shoals and shoals!' said his mother. 'I shall come back in the late autumn, maybe to this very pond and perhaps your father will come, too, to find me and play with me as he used to do. It is good to go up the rivers in the autumn! For then there are many eels coming down to the sea, and they are very delicious to eat!'

'Good-bye!' whistled the young otters, and they swam away from their mother. One went overland to the stream and swam up it. One went to the hole under the alder-roots and lay there, sad to think that their happy family life was broken. And the third went to a marshy place he knew in a withy-bed two miles off. The mother otter swam once round the pond she knew so well and then, whistling clearly, she left it and made her way to the river.

'I shall return in the autumn!' she called to the inquisitive robin. 'Look for me then!'

THE END